LAUGHABLE LIMERICKS

Laughable Limericks

Compiled by
Sara and John E. Brewton

Illustrated by Ingrid Fetz

Thomas Y. Crowell Company

NEW YORK

Copyright © 1965 by Sara and John E. Brewton
Illustrations copyright © 1965 by Ingrid Fetz
All rights reservd.

Designed by Bert Clarke

Manufactured in the United States of America

Published in Canada by
Fitzhenry & Whiteside Limited, Toronto

Library of Congress Catalog Card No. 65-16179

7   8   9   10

ISBN 0-690-48667-7
0-690-48668-5 (LB)

Grateful acknowledgment is made to the following publishers, authors, and other copyright holders for permission to reprint copyrighted material:

Appleton-Century-Crofts, Inc., for "Said the Snail to the Tortoise: 'You may,'" "There once was a provident puffin," and "A Tapir who lived in Malay," by Oliver Herford from *Century Magazine*, copyright 1911, The Century Company, and "A puppy whose hair was so flowing," "Said the condor, in tones of despair," and "Said an ominous, erudite ermine," by Oliver Herford from *Century Magazine*, copyright 1912, The Century Company; for "There was once a giraffe who said, 'What,'" from *Artful Anticks* by Oliver Herford; for "A lion emerged from his lair," and "Said a sheep to her child, 'My dear Ruth,'" from *Book of Cheerful Cats* by J. G. Francis; and for "There once was a man with a sneeze," from *When Life Is Young* by Mary Mapes Dodge. Each of these selections reprinted by permission of Appleton-Century-Crofts, Inc.

Atheneum Publishers and Eve Merriam, for "When a cub unaware being bare," "There once was a finicky ocelot," and "A Chameleon, when he's feeling blue," from *There Is No Rhyme for Silver* by Eve Merriam, copyright © 1962 by Eve Merriam, used by permission of Atheneum Publishers.

The Ben Roth Agency, Inc., and *Punch*, for "There was a young poet of Kew" and "A Scientist living at Staines," by R. J. P. Hewison; for "There was a young lady of Bright," by A. H. R. Buller; and "There was an old man who said, 'Please,' " by E. V. Knox.

Berton Braley, for "Young Frankenstein's robot invention."

The Bobbs-Merrill Company, Inc., and heirs of James Whitcomb Riley, for "Some credulous chroniclers tell us," from *Joyful Poems for Children* by James Whitcomb Riley, copyright © 1941, 1946, 1960 by Lesley Payne, Elizabeth Eitel Miesse, and Edmund H. Eitel, copyright as to illustrations © 1946, 1960, used by permission of The Bobbs-Merrill Company, Inc., and the heirs of James Whitcomb Riley.

J. M. Dent & Sons, Ltd., for British market rights to "A bugler named Dougal MacDougal," "There was an old man of Calcutta," and "There was an old miser named Clarence," from *Verses from 1929 On* by Ogden Nash, copyright 1940 by Ogden Nash.

E. P. Dutton & Co., Inc., for "The cautious, collapsible cow," from *Lyric Laughter* by Arthur Guiterman, copyright 1939, by E. P. Dutton & Co., Inc., reprinted by permission of the publishers; and for "There was an old lady named Crockett," from *Typewriter Town* by William Jay Smith, copyright © 1960 by William Jay Smith, reprinted by permission of E. P. Dutton & Co., Inc.

Follett Publishing Company, for Beatrice P. Krone's musical accompaniment to three limericks from *Voices of America* by Wolfe, Krone, and Fullerton.

Harcourt, Brace & World, Inc., for "There was a young man named Achilles," from *Piping and Panning* by Edwin Meade Robinson, reprinted by permission of Harcourt, Brace & World, Inc.

FOREWORD

LIMERICKS are a pleasure to read, to share, to sing, to write, to illustrate.

It all started when Edward Lear, landscape painter by profession, struck off with "uproarious delight" drawings and verses—later called limericks—to amuse the grandchildren of his friend the Earl of Derby.

> There was an old Derry down Derry,
> Who loved to see little folks merry;
>   So he made them a book,
>   And with laughter they shook
> At the fun of that Derry down Derry.

Ever since Lear popularized this five-line verse, the limerick shaped

> Like a small very squat butterfly
>   With its wings opened wide,
>   Lots of nectar inside,

has been amusing the young of all ages and causing them to shake with laughter. Robert Louis Stevenson, Lewis Carroll, Rudyard Kipling, Oliver Herford, Walter de la Mare, David McCord, Ogden Nash, and John Ciardi are among the authors who have kept the limerick on its merry way.

Sara Brewton
John E. Brewton

CONTENTS

A LIMERICK shapes to the eye
Like a small very squat butterfly,
    With its wings opened wide,
    Lots of nectar inside,
And a terrible urge to fly high.

—*David McCord*

BUGS, BEES, AND BIRDS

Said a crow in the top of a tree,
"What time is it getting to be?
    If it isn't yet noon
    I got here too soon,
But I'm late if it isn't yet three."

—*John Ciardi*

I SAID to a bug in the sink,
"Are you taking a swim or a drink?"
"I," said the bug,
"Am a sea-going tug.
Am I headed for land, do you think?"

"What a silly!" I said. "That's no sea—
It's a sink!"—"A sink it may be.
But I'd sooner I think
Be at sea in the sink
Than sink in the sea, sir," said he.

—*John Ciardi*

THERE ONCE was a boy of Bagdad,
An inquisitive sort of a lad.
He said, "I will see
If a sting has a bee."
And he very soon found that it had!

3

THERE WAS an old man in a tree,
Who was horribly bored by a bee;
 When they said, "Does it buzz?"
 He replied, "Yes, it does!
It's a regular brute of a bee!"

—*Edward Lear*

A LIMERICK IN BLANK VERSE

THERE WAS an old man of St. Bees,
Who was stung in the arm by a wasp;
 When asked, "Does it hurt?"
 He replied, "No, it doesn't,
I'm *so* glad it wasn't a hornet."

—*W. S. Gilbert*

A WONDERFUL BIRD is the pelican;
His bill can hold more than his belican.
 He can take in his beak
 Food enough for a week;
But I'm darned if I see how the helican!

—*Dixon Lanier Merritt*

4

THERE ONCE was a provident puffin
Who ate all the fish he could stuff in.
    Said he, " 'Tis my plan
    To eat when I can:
When there's nuffin' to eat I eat nuffin'."

—*Oliver Herford*

SAID THE CONDOR, in tones of despair:
"Not even the atmosphere's rare.
    Since man took to flying,
    It's really *too* trying,
The people one meets in the air."

—*Oliver Herford*

THERE WAS an old man who said, "Hush!
I perceive a young bird in this bush!"
    When they said, "Is it small?"
    He replied, "Not at all!
It is four times as big as the bush!"

—*Edward Lear*

THERE WAS an old man of Dumbree
Who taught little owls to drink tea;
  For he said, "To eat mice
  Is not proper or nice,"
That amiable man of Dumbree.

         —*Edward Lear*

THERE WAS an old person of Crowle,
Who lived in the nest of an owl;
When they screamed in the nest,
He screamed out with the rest,
That depressing old person of Crowle.

—*Edward Lear*

A DOUBLE LIMERICK OR TWINER

THERE WAS an old man with a gun,
Who espied an old lady named Pheasant;
She sat on a seat in the sun,
And he stared, and he stared—most unpleasant:
But at last, drawing near,
He made it quite clear
That he had no *intention* so rude to appear,
But was merely confused, being out with
his gun,
At espying a lady named Pheasant.

—*Walter De La Mare*

7

AT THE ZOO I remarked to an emu,
"I cannot pretend I esteem you.
    You're a greedy old bird,
    And your walk is absurd,
But your curious feathers redeem you."

F WAS a fussy flamingo,
Who remarked to his family, "By jingo!
    I think I would go
    To that animal show,
But they all talk such barbarous lingo."

—*Carolyn Wells*

A FLEA and a fly in a flue
Were caught, so what could they do?
    Said the fly, "Let us flee."
    "Let us fly," said the flea.
So they flew through a flaw in the flue.

CRAWLERS, CROAKERS, AND CREEPERS

THERE WAS an old man with a flute.
A "sarpint" ran into his boot;
    But he played day and night,
    Till the "sarpint" took flight,
And avoided that man with a flute.

—*Edward Lear*

"THERE'S A TUNE," said a sly Bengalese,
"Which will charm any snake that you please:
     Take a long, heavy stick;
     Hit the snake with it—quick!
Then proceed with the tune at your ease."

                        —*John Bennett*

THERE ONCE was a man who said, "Why
Can't I look that big snake in the eye?"
     The snake said, "You can,"
     And he looked at the man.
('Most any last line will apply.)

                      —*Carolyn Wells*

A CHAMELEON, when he's feeling blue,
Can alter his glum point of view
     By changing his hue
     To a color that's new:
I'd like to do that, wouldn't you?

                      —*Eve Merriam*

SAID THE SNAIL to the tortoise: "You may
Find it hard to believe what I say;
    You will think it absurd,
    But I give you my word,
They fined me for speeding today."

"Well, well!" said the tortoise. "Dear me!"
How defective your motor must be!
    Though I speed every day,
    Not a fine do I pay:
The police cannot catch me, you see."

                —Oliver Herford

THERE WAS an old person of Ickley,
Who could not abide to ride quickly;
    He rode to Karnak
    On a tortoise's back,
That moony old person of Ickley.

                —Edward Lear

ANIMALS—FRIENDLY AND TAME

A PUPPY whose hair was so flowing
There really was no means of knowing
    Which end was his head,
    Once stopped me and said,
"Please, sir, am I coming or going?"

—*Oliver Herford*

THERE WAS a young lady of Corsica,
Who purchased a little brown saucy-cur;
    Which she fed upon ham
    And hot raspberry jam,
That expensive young lady of Corsica.

—*Edward Lear*

THERE WAS an old man of Kamschatka,
Who possessed a remarkably fat cur;
    His gait and his waddle
    Were held as a model
To all the fat dogs in Kamschatka.

—*Edward Lear*

THERE ONCE were two cats of Kilkenny,
Each thought there was one cat too many;
    So they fought and they fit,
    And they scratched and they bit,
Till instead of two cats there weren't any.

A CAT in despondency sighed,
And resolved to commit suicide;
    He got under the wheels
    Of nine automobiles,
And after the last one he died.

THERE WAS a young man who was bitten
By forty-two cats and a kitten,
    Cried he, "It is clear
    My end is quite near,
No matter, I'll die like a Briton!"

THERE WAS a young man from the city,
Who met what he thought was a kitty;
    He gave it a pat,
    And said, "Nice little cat!"
And they buried his clothes out of pity.

THERE WAS a young prince of Bombay,
Who always would have his own way;
    He pampered his horses
    On five or six courses,
Himself eating nothing but hay.

—*Walter Parke*

A CERTAIN young gallant named Robbie
Rode his steed back and forth in the lobby;
    When they told him, "Indoors
    Is no place for a horse,"
He replied, "Well, you see, it's my hobby."

A MOUSE in her room woke Miss Dowd;
She was frightened and screamed very loud,
    Then a happy thought hit her—
    To scare off the critter,
She sat up in bed and meowed.

THERE WAS an old man who said, "How
Shall I flee from that horrible cow?
    I will sit on this stile,
    And continue to smile,
Which may soften the heart of that cow."

        —*Edward Lear*

THERE WAS an old soldier of Bister,
Went walking one day with his sister;
    When a cow, at one poke,
    Tossed her into an oak,
Before the old gentleman missed her.

THE CAUTIOUS collapsible cow
Gives milk by the sweat of her brow;
    Then under the trees
    She folds her front knees
And sinks fore and aft with a bow.

        —*Arthur Guiterman*

A VERY grandiloquent goat
Sat down to a gay table d'hôte;
    He ate all the corks,
    The knives and the forks,
Remarking: "On these things I dote."

Then, before his repast he began,
While pausing the menu to scan,
    He said: "Corn, if you please,
    And tomatoes and pease,
I'd like to have served in the can."

—*Carolyn Wells*

SAID A SHEEP to her child, "My dear Ruth,
Such precipitate haste is uncouth.
    When you come down a stair
    Use some caution and care,
And restrain this wild impulse of youth."

—*J. G. Francis*

THE REVEREND Henry Ward Beecher
Called a hen a most elegant creature.
    The hen, pleased with that,
    Laid an egg in his hat,—
And thus did the hen reward Beecher!

—Oliver Wendell Holmes

AN OLD LADY living in Worcester
Had a gift of a handsome young rorcester;
    But the way that it crough,
    As 'twould never get through,
Was more than the lady was uorcester.

THERE WAS an old lady of France,
Who taught little ducklings to dance;
    When she said, "Tick-a-tack!"—
    They only said, "Quack!"
Which grieved that old lady of France.

—Edward Lear

ANIMALS—NOT SO FRIENDLY AND TAME

WHEN A CUB, unaware being bare
Was the best-dressed state for a bear,
    Put on a barrel
    For wearing apparel
His mother cried, "This I can't bear!"

                     —*Eve Merriam*

A CHEERFUL OLD BEAR at the zoo
Could always find something to do.
 When it bored him to go
 On a walk to and fro,
He reversed it, and walked fro and to.

THERE WAS once a giraffe who said, "What
Do I want with my tea strong or hot?
 For my throat's such a length
 The tea loses its strength,
And is cold ere it reaches the spot."

—*Oliver Herford*

A BARBER who lived in Batavia
Was known for his fearless behavia.
 An enormous baboon
 Broke in his saloon,
But he murmured, "I'm blamed if I'll shavia."

THERE ONCE was a stately giraffe,
Whose motto was "Nothing by half!"
His old friend, the tapir,
Said, "Cut me a caper,—
It's a year since I've had a good laugh!"

So, to please him, the gracious giraffe
Jumped over a cow and her calf;
But when the old tapir
Told folks of this caper,
They said: "That's just some more of your chaff.

"He's a dignified chap, that giraffe,
And we know he does nothing by half;
We can understand how
He might jump o'er a cow,
But he'd *never* jump over a calf!"

—*Margaret Vandegrift*

L IS for lovable Lena,
Who met a ferocious hyena;
Whatever occurred
I never have heard;
But anyhow, L is for Lena.

THERE WAS an old hag of Malacca,
Who smoked such atrocious tobacca,
When tigers came near
They trembled with fear,
And didn't attempt to attacca.

A LION emerged from his lair
For a short summer cut to his hair.
But the barber he wept;
While the customers slept
As they waited their turn in the chair.

—*J. G. Francis*

31

A HANDSOME young noble of Spain,
Met a lion one day in the rain.
　　He ran in a fright
　　With all of his might,
But the lion, he ran with his mane!

ONE DAY I went out to the zoo,
For I wanted to see the old gnu,
　　But the old gnu was dead.
　　They had a new gnu instead,
And that gnu, well, he knew he was new.

—*G. T. Johnson*

THERE ONCE was a barber of Kew,
Who went very mad at the zoo;
　　He tried to enamel
　　The face of the camel,
And gave the brown bear a shampoo.

—*Cosmo Monkhouse*

A TAPIR who lived in Malay
Was reading the fall styles one day,
　　When he cried with delight,
　　"*My* figure's all right:
Tapir waists are the fashion, they say."

　　　　　　　—*Oliver Herford*

THERE ONCE was a finicky ocelot
Who all the year round was cross a lot
　　Except at Thanksgiving
　　When he enjoyed living
For he liked to eat cranberry sauce a lot.

　　　　　　　—*Eve Merriam*

THERE ONCE was an arch armadillo
Who built him a hut 'neath a willow;
　　He hadn't a bed
　　So he rested his head
On a young porcupine for a pillow.

　　　　　　　—*Carolyn Wells*

SAID AN ENVIOUS, erudite ermine:
"There's *one* thing I cannot determine:
  When a man wears my coat,
  He's a person of note,
While *I'm* but a species of vermin!"

—*Oliver Herford*

THERE ONCE was a knowing raccoon
Who didn't believe in the moon.
  "Every month—don't you see?—
  There's a new one," said he.
"No *real* moon could wear out so soon!"

—*Mary Mapes Dodge*

THERE ONCE was a plesiosaurus
Which lived when the earth was all porous.
　　But it fainted with shame
　　When it first heard its name,
And departed long ages before us.

L WAS a lachrymose leopard,
Who ate up twelve sheep and a shepherd;
　　But the real reason why
　　He continued to cry
Was his food was so lavishly peppered.

—Carolyn Wells

THERE WAS an old man of Boulak,
Who sat on a crocodile's back;
　　But they said, "Tow'rds the night
　　He may probably bite,
Which might vex you, old man of Boulak!"

—Edward Lear

THERE WAS a young angler of Worthing,
Who dug up ten worms and a fur thing.
He said, "How I wish
Eleven fine fish
Would snap up these things I'm unearthing."

AN OYSTER from Kalamazoo
Confessed he was feeling quite blue,
"For," says he, "as a rule,
When the weather turns cool,
I invariably get in a stew!"

THERE ONCE was a corpulent carp
Who wanted to play on a harp;
But to his chagrin
So short was his fin
He couldn't reach up to C sharp.

—*Carolyn Wells*

A DOUBLE LIMERICK OR TWINER

THERE WAS an old person of Dover
Who called on his sister in Deal,
With a sack hanging over his shoulder
In which was a whopping great eel.
It leapt down the area, scuttled upstairs,
It golloped up bolsters and wash-jugs and chairs,
Her boots, shoes, and slippers, in singles and pairs;
And alas! when this Ogre
Had finished its meal,
There was no-one of Dover
With a sister in Deal.

—Walter De La Mare

LAUGHS ANATOMICAL

A SMALL BOY who lived in Iquique
Had a voice irritatingly squique;
    When his father said, "Oil it,
    My son, or you'll spoil it,"
His reply was a trifle too chique.

THERE WAS a young man at the War Office,
Whose brain was an absolute store office.
    Each warning severe
    Went in at one ear,
And out at the opposite orifice.

—*J. W. Churton*

THERE WAS a young lady of Kent,
Whose nose was most awfully bent.
    One day, I suppose,
    She followed her nose,
For no one knew which way she went.

THERE WAS an old man in a barge,
Whose nose was exceedingly large;
    But in fishing by night,
    It supported a light,
Which helped that old man in a barge.

—*Edward Lear*

THERE WAS an old man with a nose,
Who said, "If you choose to suppose
  That my nose is too long,
  You are certainly wrong!"
That remarkable man with a nose.

       —Edward Lear

THERE WAS an old man of West Dumpet,
Who possessed a large nose like a trumpet;
  When he blew it aloud,
  It astonished the crowd,
And was heard through the whole of
  West Dumpet.

       —Edward Lear

THERE WAS a young lady whose nose
Continually prospers and grows;
  When it grew out of sight,
  She exclaimed in a fright,
"Oh! Farewell to the end of my nose!"

       —Edward Lear

THERE WAS an old man of Blackheath,
Who sat on his set of false teeth;
  Said he, with a start,
  "O Lord, bless my heart!
I've bitten myself underneath!"

THERE WAS an old man of Tarentum
Who gnashed his false teeth 'til he bent 'em.
  When they asked him the cost
  Of what he had lost,
He replied, "I can't say, for I rent 'em."

THERE WAS an old man of Calcutta,
Who coated his tonsils with butta,
  Thus converting his snore
  From a thunderous roar
To a soft, oleaginous mutta.

—*Ogden Nash*

43

THERE WAS a young lady whose chin
Resembled the point of a pin;
So she had it made sharp,
And purchased a harp,
And played several tunes with her chin.

—Edward Lear

FOR BEAUTY I am not a star,
There are others more handsome by far;
But my face I don't mind it,
For I am behind it,
It's the people in front that I jar.

—Anthony Euwer

THERE WAS a young curate named Stone,
Who lived by himself, quite alone.
He'd a face like a hatchet,
I defy you to match it.
Quoth he, "I don't mind—it's my own!"

—F. H. Cozens

No MATTER how grouchy you're feeling,
You'll find the smile more or less healing.
    It grows in a wreath
    All around the front teeth—
Thus preserving the face from congealing.

—*Anthony Euwer*

THERE WAS an old person of Down,
Whose face was adorned with a frown;
    When he opened the door,
    For one minute or more,
He alarmed all the people of Down.

—*Edward Lear*

I'D RATHER have fingers than toes;
I'd rather have ears than a nose;
    And as for my hair,
    I'm glad it's still there;
I'll be awfully sad when it goes!

—*Gelett Burgess*

In New Orleans there lived a young Creole,
Who, when asked if her hair were all reole,
Replied, with a shrug,
"Just give it a tug,
And judge by the way that I squeole."

V is a vain virtuoso.
If you ask, "Pray what makes your hair grow so,
Do you think it's a sign
Of genius divine?"
He replies, "I don't think so, I know so."

—*Oliver Herford*

There was an old man in a tree,
Whose whiskers were lovely to see;
But the birds of the air
Pluck'd them perfectly bare,
To make themselves nests in that tree.

—*Edward Lear*

There was an old man with a beard,
Who said, "It's just as I feared!—
    Two owls and a hen,
    Four larks and a wren,
Have all built their nests in my beard!"

—*Edward Lear*

THERE WAS a faith healer of Deal
Who said, "Although pain is not real,
        When I sit on a pin
        And it punctures my skin,
I dislike what I fancy I feel."

A PIRATE who hailed from Nertskinski
Became so exceedingly thinski
        That while cleaning his gun,
        When the day's fight was done,
He looked down the bore and fell inski.

HIS SISTER named Lucy O'Finner,
Grew constantly thinner and thinner,
        The reason was plain,
        She slept out in the rain,
And was never allowed any dinner.

—*Lewis Carroll*

THERE ONCE was a girl of New York
Whose body was lighter than cork;
 She had to be fed
 For six weeks upon lead
Before she went out for a walk.

     —*Cosmo Monkhouse*

SOME CREDULOUS chroniclers tell us
Of a very tall youngster named Ellis.
 Whose Pa said, "Ma-ri-er,
 If Bubb grows much higher,
He'll have to be trained up a trellis."

     —*James Whitcomb Riley*

THE HANDS they were made to assist
In supplying the features with grist.
 There are only a few,—
 As a rule, about two,
And are hitched to the end of the wrist.

     —*Anthony Euwer*

THERE WAS once a young man of Oporta
Who daily got shorter and shorter,
    The reason he said
    Was the hod on his head
Which was filled with the heaviest mortar.

—*Lewis Carroll*

A GIRL who weighed many an oz.
Used language I dared not pronoz.
    For a fellow unkind
    Pulled her chair out behind
Just to see (so he said) if she'd boz.

A GLOBE-TROTTING MAN from St. Paul
Made a trip to Japan in the faul.
    One thing he found out,
    As he rambled about,
Was that Japanese ladies St. Taul.

                —*Ferdinand G. Christgau*

THERE WAS an old man, who when little
Fell casually into a kettle;
    But, growing too stout,
    He could never get out,
So he passed all his life in that kettle.

                —*Edward Lear*

BEHAVIOR—SCROOBIOUS
AND STRANGE

THERE WAS an old person of Grange,
Whose manners were scroobious and strange;
He sailed to St. Blubb,
In a waterproof tub,
That aquatic old person of Grange.

—*Edward Lear*

THE AKOND OF SWAT

Who, or why, or which, or what
                    Is the Akond of Swat?

Is he tall or short, or dark, or fair?
Does he sit on a stool or a sofa or chair,
                    or SQUAT,
          The Akond of Swat?

Is he wise or foolish, young or old?
Does he drink his soup and his coffee cold,
                    or HOT,
          The Akond of Swat?

Does he sing or whistle, jabber or talk?
When riding abroad, does he gallop or walk,
                    or TROT,
          The Akond of Swat?

Does he wear a turban, a fez, or a hat?
Does he sleep on a mattress, a bed, or a mat,
                    or a COT,
          The Akond of Swat?

When he writes a copy in round-hand size,
Does he cross his t's and finish his i's
                    with a DOT,
          The Akond of Swat?

Can he write a letter concisely clear,
Without a speck or a smudge or smear
                    or BLOT,
          The Akond of Swat?

Do his people like him extremely well?
Or do they, whenever they can, rebel,
                    or PLOT,
          At the Akond of Swat?

If he catches them then, either old or young,
Does he have them chopped in pieces or hung,
                    or SHOT,
          The Akond of Swat?

Does he study the wants of his own dominion?
Or doesn't he care for public opinion
                    a JOT,
          The Akond of Swat?

To amuse his mind do his people show him
Pictures, or anyone's last new poem,
                    or WHAT,
        The Akond of Swat?

At night if he suddenly screams and wakes,
Do they bring him only a few small cakes,
                    or a LOT,
        The Akond of Swat?

Does he live on turnips, tea, or tripe?
Does he like his shawl to be marked with a stripe,
                    or a DOT,
        The Akond of Swat?

Is he quiet, or always making a fuss?
Is his steward a Swiss, or a Swede, or a Russ,
                    or a SCOT,
        The Akond of Swat?

Does he like to sit by the calm blue wave?
Or to sleep and snore in a dark green cave,
                    or a GROT,
        The Akond of Swat?

Does he drink small beer from a silver jug?
Or a bowl? or a glass? or a cup? or a mug?
                    or a POT,
        The Akond of Swat?

Does he beat his wife with a gold-topped pipe,
When she lets the gooseberries grow too ripe,
                              or ROT,
                 The Akond of Swat?

Does he wear a white tie when he dines with friends,
And tie it neat in a bow with ends,
                            or a KNOT,
                 The Akond of Swat?

Does he like new cream, and hate mince-pies?
When he looks at the sun does he wink his eyes,
                              or NOT,
                 The Akond of Swat?

Does he teach his subjects to roast and bake?
Does he sail about on an inland lake
                          in a YACHT,
                 The Akond of Swat?

Someone, or nobody, knows I wot
Who, or which, or why, or *what*
                 Is the Akond of Swat!

                                    —*Edward Lear*

A REPLY FROM THE AKOND OF SWAT

Mr. Lear, I'm the Akond of Swat;
    I am gracious and fat
    In a very tall hat
And I'm heating a very large pot—
You know why, and for whom, and for what.

          —*Ethel Talbot Scheffauer*

THERE WAS a young lady named Ruth,
Who had a great passion for truth.
She said she would die
Before she would lie,
And she died in the prime of her youth.

THERE WAS an old miser named Clarence,
Who simonized both of his parents.
"The initial expense,"
He remarked, "is immense,
But I'll save it on wearance and tearance."

—*Ogden Nash*

A SILLY YOUNG FELLOW named Hyde
In a funeral procession was spied;
When asked, "Who is dead?"
He giggled and said,
"I don't know; I just came for the ride."

THERE WAS a young fellow of Ealing,
Endowed with such delicate feeling,
When he read, on the door,
"Don't spit on the floor,"
He jumped up and spat on the ceiling.

A MAN went a-hunting at Rygate,
And wished to leap over a high gate.
Said the owner, "Go 'round,
With your gun and your hound,
For you never shall leap over *my* gate!"

THERE WAS a young person called Smarty
Who sent out his cards for a party;
So exclusive and few
Were the friends that he knew
That no one was present but Smarty.

THERE WAS an old lady who said,
When she found a thief under her bed,
"Get up from the floor;
You're too close to the door,
And I fear you'll take cold in the head."

M IS for mournful Miss Molly,
Who liked to be thought melancholy.
She's as limp as a rag
When her sisters play tag,
For it's vulgar, she says, to be jolly.

—*Isabel Frances Bellows*

THERE WAS a young farmer of Leeds,
Who swallowed six packets of seeds.
It soon came to pass
He was covered with grass,
And he couldn't sit down for the weeds.

THERE'S A DOWAGER near Sneden Landing
Whose manners are bluff and commanding;
It is one of her jests
To trip up her guests,
For she hates to keep gentlemen standing.

A RATHER POLITE MAN of Hawarden,
When taking a walk in his gawarden,
If he trod on a slug,
A worm or a bug,
Would say, "My dear friend, I beg pawarden!"

THERE WAS once a small boy in Quebec
Stood buried in snow to his neck.
When asked: "Are you friz?"
He said: "Yes, I is,
But we don't call this cold in Quebec."

—*Rudyard Kipling*

THERE WAS an old man of Khartoum
Who kept two tame sheep in his room:
"For," he said, "they remind me
Of one left behind me,
But I cannot remember of whom."

THERE ONCE was a man with a sneeze,
Who always would sit in a breeze.
When begged to take shelter
He'd cry: "I should swelter!"
And straightway go on with his sneeze.

—*Mary Mapes Dodge*

THERE WAS a young lady named Wemyss,
Who, it semyss, was troubled with dremyss.
She would wake in the night,
And, in terrible fright,
Shake the bemyss of the house with her scremyss.

THERE WAS a young man named Achilles
Whose wrongs always gave him the willies,
So he sulked in his tent
Like a half-witted gent,
Say, wasn't them heroes the sillies.

—*Edwin Meade Robinson*

AN UNPOPULAR YOUTH of Cologne,
With a pain in his stomach did mogne.
He heaved a great sigh
And said, "I would digh,
But the loss would be only my ogne."

TWO BROTHERS there were of Sioux City;
Each one thought the other tioux pretty.
So each took his knife
And the other one's klife.
Now which of the tioux dioux yioux pity?

THERE WAS a young fellow of Perth,
Who was born on the day of his birth;
    He was married, they say,
    On his wife's wedding day,
And he died when he quitted the earth.

A SKELETON once in Khartoum
Asked a spirit up into his room;
    They spent the whole night
    In the eeriest fight
As to which should be frightened of whom.

THERE ARE MEN in the village of Erith
Whom nobody seeth or heareth,
    And there looms, on the marge
    Of the river, a barge
That nobody roweth or steereth.

66

THERE WAS an old man of Thermopylae,
Who never did anything properly;
But they said, "If you choose
To boil eggs in your shoes,
You shall never remain in Thermopylae."

—*Edward Lear*

THERE WAS an old lady of Chertsey,
Who made a remarkable curtsey;
She twirled round and round
Till she sank underground,
Which distressed all the people of Chertsey.

—*Edward Lear*

THERE WAS an old person of Ischia,
Whose conduct grew friskier and friskier;
He danced hornpipes and jigs,
And ate thousands of figs,
That lively old person of Ischia.

—*Edward Lear*

THERE WAS an old man, who said, "Well!
Will *nobody* answer this bell?
    I have pulled day and night,
    Till my hair has grown white,
But nobody answers this bell!"

                        —*Edward Lear*

THERE WAS an old person of Burton,
Whose answers were rather uncertain;
    When they said, "How d'ye do?"
    He replied, "Who are you?"
That distressing old person of Burton.

                        —*Edward Lear*

THERE WAS an old person of Shoreham,
Whose habits were marked by decorum;
    He bought an umbrella,
    And sat in the cellar,
Which pleased all the people of Shoreham.

                        —*Edward Lear*

THERE WAS a young girl of Majorca
Whose aunt was a very fast walker;
    She walked sixty miles
    And leaped fifteen stiles,
Which astonished that girl of Majorca.

—Edward Lear

THERE WAS a young lady of Russia,
Who screamed so that no one could hush her;
    Her screams were extreme,
    No one heard such a scream,
As was screamed by that lady of Russia.

—Edward Lear

A CANNER, exceedingly canny,
One morning remarked to his granny,
    "A canner can can
    Anything that he can,
But a canner can't can a can, can he?"

—Carolyn Wells

A FELLOW who slaughtered two toucans,
Said, "I shall put them into two cans."
Two canners who heard,
Said, "You'll be a bird,
If you can put two toucans in two cans."

THERE WAS an old lady named Carr
Who took the 3:3 to Forfar;
For she said: "I conceive
It is likely to leave
Far before the 4:4 to Forfar."

THERE WAS a young lady from Woosester
Who ussessed to crow like a roosester.
She ussessed to climb
Seven trees at a time—
But her sisester ussessed to boosester.

E IS the egotist dread
Who, as someone has wittily said,
  Will talk till he's blue
  About *himself* when you
Want to talk about *yourself* instead.

      —Oliver Herford

O IS an optimist glad
Who doesn't know how to be sad.
  If he wakes up some day
  In Hades, he'll say,
"Well really it isn't so bad!"

      —Oliver Herford

P's A poetical bore
Who recites his own lines by the score.
  The ladies, poor dears,
  Are all moved to tears
And strong men are moved—to the door.

      —Oliver Herford

ACCIDENTS—MORE OR LESS FATAL

THERE WAS a young fellow named Hall,
Who fell in the spring in the fall;
    'Twould have been a sad thing
    If he'd died in the spring,
But he didn't—he died in the fall.

THERE WAS an old lady named Crockett
Who went to put a plug in a socket;
But her hands were so wet
She flew up like a jet
And came roaring back down like a rocket!

—*William Jay Smith*

HERE's little Jim Nast of Pawtucket
Who slid down the stairs in a bucket.
He has more understanding
Since reaching the landing,
Just look at the hole where he struck it.

—*Hugh Lofting*

THERE WAS a young man of Herne Bay,
Who was making explosives one day;
But he dropped his cigar
In the gunpowder jar.
There *was* a young man of Herne Bay.

THERE WAS a young fellow named Weir,
Who hadn't an atom of fear;
    He indulged a desire
    To touch a live wire;
('Most any old line will do here!)

A DARING YOUNG LADY of Guam
Observed, "The Pacific's so calm
    I'll swim out for a lark."
    She met a large shark . . .
Let us now sing the Ninetieth Psalm.

THERE WAS an old man in a boat,
Who said, "I'm afloat! I'm afloat!"
    When they said, "No, you ain't!"
    He was ready to faint,
That unhappy old man in a boat.

—*Edward Lear*

THERE WAS a wee girl named Estella
Who owned an enormous umbrella;
    Till one day in a gale
    With lightning and hail
The umbrella went up with Estella.

                  —*Mabel B. Hill*

SAID A foolish young lady of Wales,
"A smell of escaped gas prevails."
    Then she searched with a light,
    And later that night
Was collected—in seventeen pails!

                —*Langford Reed*

A DECREPIT old gas man named Peter,
While hunting around for the meter,
    Touched a leak with his light;
    He rose out of sight,
And, as everyone who knows anything
    about poetry can tell you, he also
    ruined the meter.

THERE WAS once a most charming young miss
Who considered her ice-skating bliss;
But one day, alack!
Her skates, they were slack,
And she ended up something like this.

A LITTLE BOY down in Natchez
Sat upon powder and matchez;
For the seat of war
He hankers no more,
Though re-enforced well with patchez.

A CERTAIN YOUNG MAN of great gumption,
'Mongst cannibals had the presumption
To go—but alack!
He never came back.
They say 'twas a case of consumption.

78

A NEW SERVANT MAID named Maria,
Had trouble in lighting the fire.
    The wood it was green,
      So she used gasoline,
And she's gone where the fuel is dryer.

THEY SAY that ex-President Taft
When hit by a golf ball once laughed
    And said, "I'm not sore,
      But although you cried 'Fore'
The place where you hit me was aft."

WHEN a jolly young fisher named Fisher
Went fishing for fish in a fissure,
    A fish, with a grin,
      Pulled the fisherman in.
Now they're fishing the fissure for Fisher.

79

FOOD AND EATING

A DINER while dining at Crewe,
Found quite a large mouse in his stew.
    Said the waiter, "Don't shout,
    And wave it about,
Or the rest will be wanting one, too."

THERE WAS an old man from the Rhine
Who was asked at what hour he would dine.
He replied, "At eleven,
At three, six, and seven,
At eight and a quarter of nine."

THERE WAS a young man so benighted
He didn't know when he was slighted.
He went to a party
And ate just as hearty
As if he'd been really invited.

THERE WAS a young man of Calcutta
Who spoke with a terrible stutta.
At breakfast he said,
"Give me b-b-b-bread
And b-b-b-b-b-b-butta."

THERE ONCE was a bonnie Scotch laddie,
Who said, as he put on his pladie:
    "I've just had a dish
    O' unco' guid fish."
What had 'e had? Had 'e had haddie?

THERE'S NOTHING in afternoon tea
To appeal to a person like me;
    There is little to eat;
    What there is is too sweet;
And I feel like a cow in a tree.

—*Gelett Burgess*

SAID A bad little youngster named Beauchamp:
"Those jelly-tarts, how shall I reauchamp?
    To my parents I'd go,
    But they always say 'No,'
No matter how much I beseauchamp."

—*Carolyn Wells*

A CHEESE that was aged and gray
Was walking and talking one day.
   Said the cheese, "Kindly note
   My mama was a goat
And I'm made out of curds by the whey."

THERE WAS a young lady named Perkins,
Who had a great fondness for gherkins;
   She went to a tea
   And ate twenty-three,
Which pickled her internal workin's.

THE WAITER said: "Try the ragout,"
When asked to suggest something nout;
   Then said to the cook,
   With a sly backward look;
"The gent wants a bowl of beef stout."

THERE'S A LADY in Kalamazoo,
Who bites all her oysters in two;
　　She has a misgiving,
　　Should any be living,
They'd raise such a hullabaloo.

　　　　　　　—*William Bellamy*

THERE'S A GIRL out in Ann Arbor, Mich.,
To meet whom I never would wich.;
　　She'd eat up ice cream
　　Till with colic she'd scream,
Then order another big dich.

THERE WAS an old man who said, "Please
Give me some of that excellent cheese.
　　I have smelt it for miles,
　　Coming over the stiles
To your beautiful house on the Tees."

　　　　　　　—*E. V. Knox*
　　　　　　("Evoe" of *Punch*)

There was an old lady of Rye,
Who was baked by mistake in a pie;
    To the household's disgust
    She emerged through the crust,
And exclaimed, with a yawn, "Where am I?"

THERE WAS an old lady of Brooking,
Who had a great genius for cooking;
    She could bake sixty pies
    All quite the same size,
And tell which was which without looking.

THERE WAS an old person of Dean,
Who dined on one pea and one bean;
    For he said, "More than that
    Would make me too fat,"
That cautious old person of Dean.

—Edward Lear

THERE ONCE was a pious young priest
Who lived almost wholly on yeast;
    "For," he said, "it is plain
    We must all rise again,
And I want to get started, at least."

THE PRINCIPAL FOOD of the Sioux
Is Indian maize, which they brioux
And hominy make,
Or mix in a cake,
And eat it with fork, as they chioux.

THERE IS an old cook in N. Y.
Who insists you should always st. p.;
He says he once tried
To eat some that was fried,
And claims he would rather ch. c.

CLOTHING AND DRESS

THERE WAS an old lady whose folly
Induced her to sit in a holly;
    Whereon by a thorn,
    Her dress being torn,
She quickly became melancholy.

—*Edward Lear*

THERE WAS a young man of Bengal,
Who went to a fancy dress ball;
    He went, just for fun,
    Dressed up as a bun,
And a dog ate him up in the hall.

A SLEEPER from the Amazon
Put nighties of his gra'mazon—
    The reason, that
    He was too fat
To get his own pajamazon.

THERE WAS an old man of the Cape,
Who made himself garments of crêpe.
    When asked, "Do they tear?"
    He replied, "Here and there,
But they're perfectly splendid for shape!"

               —*Robert Louis Stevenson*

THERE WAS a young person of Crete,
Whose toilet was far from complete;
    She dressed in a sack
    Spickle-speckled with black,
That ombliferous person of Crete.

—*Edward Lear*

AN IMPORTANT young man of Quebec
Had to welcome the Duchess of Teck;
    So he bought for a dollar
    A very high collar
To save himself washing his neck.

—*J. H. Pitman*

THERE WAS an old person of Fratton
Who would go to church with his hat on.
    "If I wake up," he said,
    "With my hat on my head,
I shall know that it hasn't been sat on."

THERE WAS a young lady of Durban
Who insisted on wearing a turban.
    When asked why she wore it,
    She said, "I adore it;
I'm weary of fashions suburban."

THERE WAS a young woman of Ayr,
Tried to steal out of church during prayer,
    But the squeak of her shoes
    So enlivened the pews
That she sat down again in despair.

THERE WAS an old man of Toulouse,
Who purchased a new pair of shoes;
    When asked, "Are they pleasant?"—
    He said, "Not at present!"
That turbid old man of Toulouse.

—*Edward Lear*

A CHARMING OLD LADY of Settle,
Instead of a hat, wore a kettle.
 When the people derided,
 She said, "I've decided
To show all the neighbors my mettle."

—*Edward Lear*

THERE WAS a young lady whose bonnet
Came untied when the birds sat upon it;
    But she said, "I don't care!
    All the birds in the air
Are welcome to sit on my bonnet!"

THE POOR benighted Hindoo,
He does the best he kindo;
    He sticks to caste
    From first to last;
For pants he makes his skindo.

—Cosmo Monkhouse

A WANDERING TRIBE called the Sioux,
Wear moccasins, having no shioux,
    They are made of buckskin,
    With the fleshy side in,
Embroidered with beads of bright hyioux.

SCHOOL AND COLLEGE

A TEACHER whose spelling's unique
Thus wrote down the "Days of the Wique":
    The first he spelt "Sonday,"
    The second day, "Munday"—
And now a new teacher they sique.

—*Charles Battell Loomis*

SAID A BOY to his teacher one day:
"Wright has not written rite right, I say."
  And the teacher replied,
  As the blunder she eyed: —
"Right!—Wright, write rite right, right away!"

A SMALL BOY when asked to spell "yacht,"
Most saucily said, "I will nacht."
  So his teacher in wrath,
  Took a section of lath,
And warmed him up well on the spacht.

A BOY at Sault Ste. Marie
Said, "Spelling is all Greek to me,
  Till they learn to spell 'Soo'
  Without any 'u,'
Or an 'a' or an 'l' or a 't.' "

A BRANCH LIBRARY

There is an old fellow named Mark,
Who lives in a tree in the park.
    You can see him each night,
    By his library light,
Turning over the leaves after dark.

—*James Montgomery Flagg*

THERE'S A very mean man of Belsize,
Who thinks he is clever and wise.
    And, what do you think,
    He saves gallons of ink
By simply not dotting his "i's."

A MEDICAL STUDENT named Elias,
Who woke just as Professor Zacharias
    Announced from his treatise:
    "I think diabetes—"
Yelled: "Beat us? They can't even tie us!"

A COLLEGIATE DAMSEL named Breeze,
Weighed down by B. A.'s and Litt. D.'s,
    Collapsed from the strain.
    Alas, it was plain
She was killing herself—by degrees.

MUSIC AND MUSICIANS

A BUGLER named Dougal MacDougal
Found ingenious ways to be frugal.
  He learned how to sneeze
  In various keys,
Thus saving the price of a bugle.

—*Ogden Nash*

THERE WAS a composer named Bong
Who composed a new popular song.
It was simply the croon
Of a lovesick baboon,
With occasional thumps on the gong.

OF A SUDDEN the great prima-donna
Cried, "Heavens! my voice is a goner!"
But a cat in the wings
Cried, "I know how she sings,"
And finished the solo with honor.

—*Paul West*

THERE WAS a young girl in the choir
Whose voice rose hoir and hoir,
Till it reached such a height
It was clear out of sight,
And they found it next day in the spoir.

A MUSICAL LADY from Ga.,
Once sang in "Lucretia Ba."
    Said a friend the next day,
    "I'm sorry to say
That high note in C major fla."

THERE WAS a composer named Liszt
Who from writing could seldom desiszt.
    He made Polonaise
    Quite worthy of praise,
And now that he's gone, he is miszt.

A MODERN COMPOSER named Brahms,
Caused in music the greatest of quahms,
    His themes so complex
    Every critic would vex,
From symphonies clear up to psahms.

THERE WAS a composer named Haydn,
The field of sonata would waydn;
    He wrote *The Creation*
    Which made a sensation,
And this was the work which he daydn.

A BOY who played tunes on a comb,
Had become such a nuisance at homb,
    That ma spanked him, and then—
    "Will you do it again?"
And he cheerfully answered her, "Nomb."

SCIENCE
AND MATHEMATICS

RELATIVITY AND LEVITATION

I WISH that my room had a floor,
I don't so much care for a door,
    But this walking around
    Without touching the ground,
Is getting to be quite a bore!

—*Gelett Burgess*

A SCIENTIST living at Staines
Is searching with infinite pains
    For a new type of sound
    Which he hopes, when it's found,
Will travel much faster than planes.

R. J. P. Hewison

INTERPLANETARY LIMERICK

A MARTIAN named Harrison Harris
Decided he'd like to see Paris;
    In space (so we learn)
    He forgot where to turn—
And that's why he's now on Polaris.

—Al Graham

YOUNG FRANKENSTEIN's robot invention
Caused trouble too awful to mention.
    Its actions were ghoulish,
    Which proves it is foolish
To monkey with Nature's intention.

—Berton Braley

THERE WAS a young man from Trinity
Who solved the square root of infinity.
While counting the digits,
He was seized by the fidgets,
Dropped science, and took up divinity.

THERE WAS an old man who said, "Gee!
I can't multiply seven by three!
Though fourteen seems plenty,
It might come to twenty—
I haven't the slightest idee!"

THERE WAS an old man who said, "Do
Tell me how I should add two and two?
I think more and more
That it makes about four—
But I fear that is almost too few."

SAID Mrs. Isosceles Tri,
"That I'm sharp I've no wish to deny;
But I do not dare
To be perfectly square—
I'm sure if I did I should die!"

—*Clinton Brooks Burgess*

THERE WAS a young man of Cadiz
Who inferred that life is what it is;
For he early had learnt,
If it were what it weren't,
It could not be that which it is.

ON MONSIEUR COUÉ

THIS VERY remarkable man
Commends a most practical plan:
You can do what you want
If you don't think you can't,
So don't think you can't think you can.

—*Charles Cuthbert Inge*

COURTSHIP

THERE ONCE was a maiden of Siam
Who said to her lover, young Kiam,
    "If you kiss me, of course,
    You will have to use force,
But Lord knows you are stronger than I am."

THERE's A tiresome young man in Bay Shore;
When his fiancée cried, "I adore
    The beautiful sea!"
    He replied, "I agree
It's pretty; but what is it for?"

A SPORTY YOUNG MAN in St. Pierre
Had a sweetheart and oft went to sierre.
    She was Gladys by name,
    And one time when he came
Her mother said: "Gladys St. Hierre."

                —*Ferdinand G. Christgau*

THOUGH A young man of football physique,
His heart was exceedingly wique,
    While he much loved the maid
    He was so afraid
That he hadn't the courage to spique.

THERE WAS an old man of Nantucket
Who kept all his cash in a bucket;
   But his daughter, named Nan,
   Ran away with a man,
And as for the bucket, Nantucket.

—*Princeton Tiger*

PA FOLLOWED the pair to Pawtucket
(The man and the girl with the bucket)
   And he said to the man,
   "You're welcome to Nan."
But as for the bucket, Pawtucket.

—*Chicago Tribune*

A LADY there was of Antigua,
Who said to her spouse, "What a pig you are!"
   He answered, "My queen,
   Is it manners you mean,
Or do you refer to my figuah?"

—*Cosmo Monkhouse*

COURTSHIP

A YOUNG LADY sings in our choir
Whose hair is the color of phoir,
But her charm is unique,
She has such a fair chique,
It is really a joy to be nhoir.

Whenever she looks down the aisle
She gives me a beautiful smaisle,
And of all her beaux,
I am certain she sheaux
She likes me the best all the whaisle.

Some day, ere she grows too antique,
In marriage her hand I shall sique;
If she's not a coquette,
Which I'd greatly regruette,
She shall share my $6 a wique.

THERE WAS a young lady of station,
"I love man!" was her sole exclamation;
　　But when men cried: "You flatter,"
　　She replied: "Oh! no matter,
Isle of Man is the true explanation!"

—Lewis Carroll

THERE WAS a young lady of Harwich,
Who behaved very bad at her marwich;
　　She proceeded on skates
　　To the parish church gates,
While her friends followed on in the carwich.

A CERTAIN young fellow named Beebee
Wished to wed with a lady named Phoebe.
　　"But," said he, "I must see
　　What the clerical fee
Be before Phoebe be Phoebe Beebee."

SHE FROWNED and called him Mr.
Because in sport he kr.
And so, in spite
That very night
This Mr. kr. sr.

THERE WAS a young person named Tate
Who dined with his girl at 8:8.
But I'd hate to relate
What that fellow named Tate
And his tête-à-tête ate at 8:8.

—*Carolyn Wells*

THE BOTTLE of perfume that Willie sent
Was highly displeasing to Millicent;
Her thanks were so cold
They quarreled, I'm told,
Through that silly scent Willie sent Millicent.

WRITING LIMERICKS

～～～～～～

THE LIMERICK's lively to write:
Five lines to it—all nice and tight.
    Two long ones, two trick
    Little short ones; then quick
As a flash here's the last one in sight.

—*David McCord*

LIMERICKS ARE INTERESTING TO WRITE

WRITING LIMERICKS *has been a popular pastime of amateurs as well as of professional writers. Limericks are fascinating to make up.*

Would you like to join in the fun? If so, let David McCord, an accomplished writer of limericks, help you. In the following fourteen limericks, he not only tells you how to write a limerick but also gives you examples of the various types you may make up.

SOME LIMERICKS—most of them, reely—
Make rimes fit some key word like *Greely*
    (A man) of *Dubuque*
    (Rimed with cucumber—cuque)
Or a Sealyham (dog). Here it's *Seely*.

              —David McCord

THERE ONCE was a scarecrow named Joel
Who couldn't scare crows, save his soel.
    But the crows put the scare
    Into Joel. He's not there
Any more. That's his hat on the poel.

              —David McCord

"THERE WAS an old man" of wherever
You like, thus the limerick never
    Accounts for the young:
    You will find him unsung
Whether stupid, wise, foolish, or clever.

              —David McCord

THERE WAS a young man, let me say,
Of West Pumpkinville, Maine, U.S.A.
    You tell me there's not
    Such a place? Thanks a lot.
I forget what he did anyway.

—David McCord

TAKE THE CURIOUS CASE of Tom Pettigrew
And Hetty, his sister. When Hettigrew
    As tall as a tree
    She came just to Tom's knee.
And did *Tom* keep on growing? You bettigrew.

—David McCord

CONSIDER this odd little snail
Who lives on the rim of a pail:
    Often wet, never drowned,
    He is always around
Safe and sound, sticking tight to his trail.

—David McCord

A MAN who was fond of his skunk
Thought he smelled pure and pungent as punk.
    But his friends cried No, no,
    No, no, no, no, no, *no!*
He just stinks, or he stank, or he stunk.

—*David McCord*

THERE WAS an old man who cried Boo!
Not to me or to he but to you.
    He also said scat
    To a dog not a cat,
And to Timbuc he added too-too.

—*David McCord*

"THIS SEASON our tunnips was red
And them beets was all white. And instead
    Of green cabbages, what
    You suspect that we got?"
"I don't know." "Didn't plant none," he said.

—*David McCord*

IT's BEEN a bad year for the moles
Who live just in stockings with holes;
    And bad for the mice
    Who prefer their boiled rice
Served in shoes that don't have any soles.

          —*David McCord*

THERE ONCE was a man in the Moon,
But he got there a little too soon.
    Some others came later
    And fell down a crater—
When *was* it? Next August? Last June?

          —*David McCord*

I DON'T MUCH exactly quite care
For these cats with short ears and long hair;
    But if anything's worse
    It's the very reverse:
Just you ask any mouse anywhere.

—David McCord

So BY CHANCE it may be you've not heard
Of a small sort of queer silent bird.
    Not a song, trill, or note
    Ever comes from his throat.
If it does, I take back every word.

—David McCord

WRITE A LIMERICK NOW. Say there was
An old man of some place, what he does,
Or perhaps what he doesn't,
Or isn't or wasn't.
Want help with it? Give me a buzz.

—*David McCord*

THERE WAS a young bard of Japan
Whose limericks never would scan;
When they said it was so,
He replied: "Yes, I know,
But I make a rule of always trying to get
just as many words into the last line as
I possibly can."

THERE WAS a young poet of Kew,
Who failed to emerge into view.
So he said, "I'll dispense
With rhyme, meter, and sense,"
And he did, and he's now in "Who's Who."

TRY SINGING THESE

~~~~~~~~

AN OPERA STAR named Maria
Always tried to sing higher and higher,
    Till she hit a high note
    Which got stuck in her throat—
Then she entered the Heavenly Choir.

THERE WAS A YOUNG GIRL, A SWEET LAMB

OLD TUNE

One lilt per measure

1. There was a young girl, a sweet lamb, _____
2. There was a young la - dy of Ni - ger _____
3. There was an old maid from Pe - ru, _____
4. There was a young la - dy from Lynn, _____

Who smiled as she en - tered a tram. _____
Who smiled as she rode on a ti - ger. _____
Who thir - ty - one lan - guag - es knew; _____
Who was so ex - ceed - ing - ly thin, _____

Af - ter she had em - barked the con - duc - tor re -
They re - turned from the ride with the la - dy in -
With one pair of lungs She worked thir - ty - two
That when she es - sayed To drink lem - on -

marked, "Your fare." And she said, "Yes, I am." _____
side And the smile on the face of the ti - ger. _____
tongues, I don't won - der she's sin - gle, do you? _____
ade, She slipped thru the straw and fell in. _____

136

THERE WAS AN OLD LADY OF STEEN

BEATRICE P. KRONE

With two swings per measure

1. There was an old la - dy of Steen, ___
2. There was a young la - dy of Bright, ___
3. There was a young la - dy of Nor - way,

Whose mu - si - cal sense was not keen; ___
Whose speed was far fas - ter than light. ___
Who cas - ual - ly sat in a door - way;

She said, "Well, it's odd but I can - not tell
She set out one day in a rel - a - tive
When the door squeezed her flat, She ex - claimed, "What of

"God save the Wea - sel" from "Pop goes the Queen." ___
way, And re - turned home the pre - vi - ous night. ___
that?" This cou - ra - geous young la - dy of Nor - way.

2. *A. H. Reginald Buller*
3. *Edward Lear*

INDEX OF AUTHORS

INDEX OF FIRST LINES

143

ABOUT THE AUTHORS

Sara and John E. Brewton have been interested, for many years, in collecting poetry and verse for children. *Laughable Limericks* has grown out of this interest.

Mrs. Brewton was born in Americus, Georgia, and was graduated from the State Normal School in Athens. Dr. Brewton was born in Brewton, Alabama; he was graduated from Howard College in Birmingham, and received his M.A. and Ph.D. from George Peabody College for Teachers in Nashville, Tennessee, where he is chairman of the English Department. He has also done graduate work at Columbia University.

The Brewtons are also folklore enthusiasts, and they both enjoy gardening in their spare time.

ABOUT THE ILLUSTRATOR

Ingrid Fetz attended the Workshop School of Advertising and Editorial Art in New York City, Columbia University, and the Cambridge (Massachusetts) School of Art. She has taught art for a number of years to both children and adults. She has also been director of the Cambridge Art Center for Children.

Miss Fetz's illustrations have appeared in numerous magazines, newspapers, and books. She lives in Ossining, New York.